# More Than a Month of Sundays

A *For Better or For Worse*® Sunday Collection

## by Lynn Johnston

**Andrews and McMeel, Inc.**
*A Universal Press Syndicate Company*
**Kansas City • New York**

ISBN: 0-8362-1218-5

Library of Congress Catalog Card Number: 83-71756

September 9, 1979

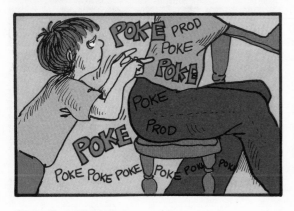

September 16, 1979

September 23, 1979

September 30, 1979

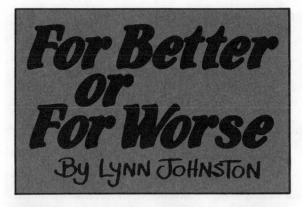

For Better or For Worse

By Lynn Johnston

October 7, 1979

October 14, 1979

October 21, 1979

# For Better or For Worse

By Lynn Johnston

IS MY COSTUME READY YET, MA? **MA?**.. IS IT DONE, MA? HUH?.. MA?

WHAT'S ALL THIS?

SPACEMEN DON'T LOOK LIKE THIS! THIS IS YUCCKY!

MICHAEL! I'VE WORKED 2 DAYS ON THIS ... AND IT LOOKS LIKE A SPACE SUIT TO ME!

.. THE ZORGONS HAVE LONGER CAPES, MA! — AND TAKE THAT DUMB STUFF OFF THE SLEEVES...

FINE. THE TAILOR SHOP IS CLOSED.

THAT'S THAT. I DON'T WANT TO TALK ABOUT THIS.. AND I ABSOLUTELY REFUSE TO GET ANGRY!

MOTHERS ARE ALWAYS MOST DANGEROUS WHEN THEY ABSOLUTELY REFUSE TO GET ANGRY...

October 28, 1979

November 11, 1979

November 18, 1979

December 16, 1979

January 6, 1980

January 27, 1980

February 10, 1980

February 24, 1980

# For Better or For Worse

## By Lynn Johnston

MOM... I KNOW... I JUST KNOW YOU'RE GOING TO BE MAD AT ME.

WHAT HAPPENED, HONEY? TELL ME WHAT IT IS.

I'M SCARED TO TELL YOU - MA... I KNOW YOU'RE GOING TO BE MAD! YOU'RE GOING TO **HATE** ME, MA!! PLEASE DON'T HATE ME, PLEASE!

MICHAEL... I WANT YOU TO BE ABLE TO TRUST US WITH YOUR PROBLEMS...

YOU'RE EXPECTING ME TO BE ANGRY & I DON'T EVEN KNOW WHAT'S HAPPENED. TELL ME, SWEETHEART...

I DREW ALL OVER THE NEW COUCH WITH FELT PENS.

LYNN JOHNSTON

March 2, 1980

March 9, 1980

March 16, 1980

March 30, 1980

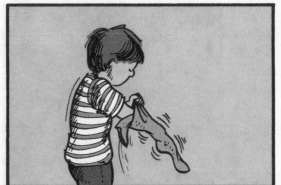

April 13, 1980

May 4, 1980

May 18, 1980

June 8, 1980

June 15, 1980

June 22, 1980

# For Better or For Worse

## By Lynn Johnston

FLIGHT NO. 108 FROM VANCOUVER IS NOW ARRIVING AT GATE 5

MACLEAN'S

IT'S DADDY!

GRANDMA'D LET ME HAVE SOME CANDY, DADDY... COME ON — PLEEEEASE?

SCREECH!

WELL, MICHAEL... DID YOU ENJOY YOUR STAY WITH GRANDMA AND GRAMPS?

YEAH. — AND GRAMPA LET ME RIDE IN THE FRONT!... I WANNA RIDE IN FRONT!

GRANDMA NEVER MADE ME EAT VEGETABLES, AN' SHE NEVER GOT MAD AT LIZZIE FOR SPILLING MILK!

GRAMPA EVEN TOLD MOM SHE NAGGED ME TOO MUCH — IT WAS NEAT!

WHEN MOM WASN'T LISTENING, THEY LET US DO ALMOST ANYTHING WE WANTED. — IT WAS WONDERFUL!

HOW LONG WILL IT TAKE TO UNDO THIS WONDERFULNESS?

June 29, 1980

July 6, 1980

July 20, 1980

August 10, 1980

August 24, 1980

September 14, 1980

September 21, 1980

# For Better or For Worse
## By Lynn Johnston

I DON'T BELIEVE WHAT I'M SEEING!

FOR WEEKS, MY WIFE COMPLAINS THAT NOBODY DOES THE WORK AROUND HERE BUT HER!

ELLY, OUT OF SHEER GUILT, I'VE HIRED A COMPANY TO CLEAN THE ENTIRE PLACE TODAY!

I KNOW

THEN WHAT ON EARTH ARE YOU DOING!!!

DO YOU EXPECT ME TO LET COMPLETE STRANGERS INTO A DIRTY HOUSE!?

September 28, 1980

October 5, 1980

November 2, 1980

# For Better or For Worse

By Lynn Johnston

BEDTIME, MICHAEL.

NO, DADDY... I DON'T **WANNA** GO TO BED!

IT'S NOT FAIR! GROWNUPS GET TO STAY UP ALL THEY WANT— BUT US KIDS HAVE TO GO TO BED EARLY!

GIVE ME ONE GOOD REASON WHY I GOTTA GO TO BED!

GROWL

IT WAS THE BEST REASON I COULD THINK OF.

November 16, 1980

# For Better or For Worse

## By Lynn Johnston

November 23, 1980

November 30, 1980

December 7, 1980

December 14, 1980

December 21, 1980

December 28, 1980

January 4, 1981

January 11, 1981

January 25, 1981

February 1, 1981

February 8, 1981

February 15, 1981

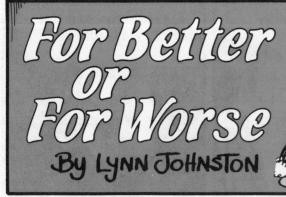

February 22, 1981

March 8, 1981

April 12, 1981

# For Better or For Worse

## By Lynn Johnston

I'LL TRADE YA A **REAL** HARD BOILED EGG FOR A CHOCOLATE ONE, LIZ....

MICHAEL— I THOUGHT YOU BOUGHT ELIZABETH A CHOCOLATE EASTER BUNNY YESTERDAY. WHERE IS IT?

WELL, I HAD TO MAKE SURE IT WAS A GOOD ONE, SO I ATE THE EARS.

THEN IT LOOKED KINDA DUMB WITHOUT THE EARS, SO I ATE THE HEAD.

I DIDN'T MEAN TO EAT THE BODY, BUT SOMETHING JUST CAME OVER ME!

I ALMOST SAVED HER THE FEET... BUT THAT WOULD HAVE BEEN A DUMB PRESENT.

ANYWAYS... DON'T YOU ALWAYS SAY "IT'S THE THOUGHT THAT COUNTS"?

April 19, 1981

# For Better or For Worse
## By Lynn Johnston

CRINKLE CRUMPLE! CRUNCH

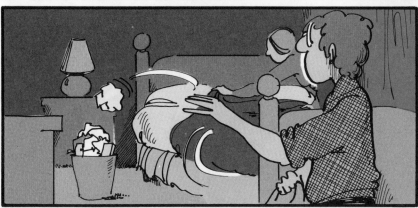

ROLL

JOHN, WHY DIDN'T YOU JUST EMPTY THE WASTE BASKET?

...YOU CAN STILL GET SOMETHING INTO IT.

Lynn

April 26, 1981

May 3, 1981

# For Better or For Worse
## By Lynn Johnston

HONEY, I WANT TO TALK TO YOU!

MICHAEL, YOU'RE A BIG, CLEVER BOY NOW.

DADDY AND I FEEL IT'S TIME WE GAVE YOU SOME GROWN UP RESPONSIBILITY.

FROM NOW ON, YOUR JOBS WILL BE SETTING AND CLEARING THE TABLE, KEEPING THE SHOE CORNER TIDY AND PUTTING AWAY YOUR OWN LAUNDRY!

I GUESS I REALLY AM A BIG KID NOW!

ELLY! – MICHAEL'S ACTUALLY DOING THOSE CHORES YOU GAVE HIM!

WHATEVER YOU SAID – SURE WORKED!

YEAH. TROUBLE IS – THAT PLOY ONLY WORKS ONCE.

May 17, 1981

May 31, 1981

June 14, 1981

# For Better or For Worse

By Lynn Johnston

MMM... THAT WAS DELICIOUS!

DESSERT?

OH, NO... I COULDN'T.

I'LL HAVE THE STRAWBERRY MOCHA PARFAIT, PLEASE!

NO, NOTHING ELSE FOR ME. YES, I'M SURE. NOTHING.

DO YOU SUPPOSE I COULD HAVE A LITTLE BITTY TASTE?

MMM... JUST ANOTHER TEENY NIBBLE...

YOU WOULDN'T MIND IF I HAD A LEEETLE BIT MORE?

HERE. TAKE THE WHOLE THING.

WHAT ARE YOU DOING? I SAID I DIDN'T WANT DESSERT!!

June 21, 1981

June 28, 1981

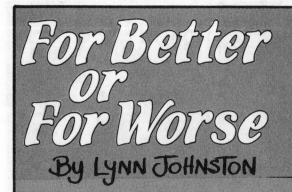

# For Better or For Worse

### By Lynn Johnston

I GUESS I'VE GOT TO FACE FACTS.

IT'S TRUE.

I REALLY AM LOOKING OLD.

I'VE GOT TO ACCEPT THE FACT THAT I'M NO LONGER "YOUNG"

I WISH IT DIDN'T MATTER. I WISH I DIDN'T CARE ABOUT IT.

WHAT ARE YOU LOOKING AT, MOM?

OH.... THE LINES ON MY FACE.

WHAT'S WRONG WITH THEM? I LIKE THE LINES ON YOUR FACE!

YOU'VE GOT A SMILE — WITH BRACKETS!

LYNN

# For Better or For Worse

### By Lynn Johnston

HI, MOM!

LIZZIE AN' I ARE PLAYING HOUSE!

I'M THE DAD, AN' LIZZIE IS THE MOM. SHE'S DOING THE WASHING AND MAKIN' SUPPER!

I DON'T SEE ANY DOLLIES—SO WHY DOESN'T ELIZABETH HAVE A JOB TOO?

LIZZIE...YOU COULD BE A POLICE LADY OR A BUS DRIVER OR A DOCTOR OR A

WAAAH! I WANNA BE THE MOMMY! I WANNA 'TAY HOME AN' MAKE SUPPER FOR MICHAEL!!

SO MUCH FOR THE GREAT REVOLUTION.

**For Better or For Worse**

By Lynn Johnston

NO DADDY!

O.K., KIDS – IT'S MY TURN TO WATCH THE T.V. – AND I WANT TO WATCH THE NEWS.

AW!

– BUT SESAME STREET IS ON AN' MR. ROGERS AN'–

I'M WATCHING THE NEWS.

WHINE

LOOK, WHO OWNS THIS T.V.? WHO LOOKS AFTER IT? WHO PAYS FOR THE REPAIRS AND THE ELECTRICITY?

YOU WATCH YOUR SHOWS ALL DAY... AND I AM ASKING FOR ONE HOUR TO WATCH THE NEWS.

UNFAIR!

NO MATTER HOW FAIR I AM... I'M STILL UNFAIR!

August 30, 1981

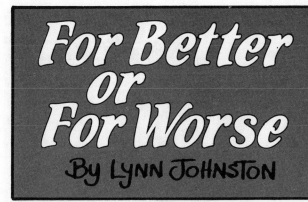

# For Better or For Worse
## By Lynn Johnston

ELLY?

UH-HUH

HONEY, I CAN'T SLEEP—WOULD YOU RUB MY BACK?

MFF-GZZ... I'M HALF ASLEEP, JOHN.

MY MOTHER USED TO RUB MY BACK AND NOW I CAN'T SLEEP SOMETIMES UNLESS...

OK, OK- BLAME MY MOTHER – SHE STARTED AN INCURABLE HABIT.

BUT IF YOU REALLY LOVED ME...

A MAN IN NEED OF A BACKRUB WILL STOOP TO ANYTHING.

September 13, 1981

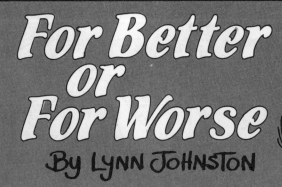

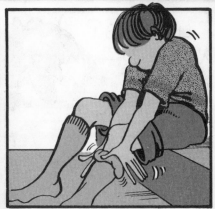

MICHAEL, I HAVE FOUND A FILTHY SOCK ON EVERY DOOR KNOB IN THE HOUSE !!!

GREAT. I THOUGHT I'D FORGOTTEN A COUPLE.

October 4, 1981

November 1, 1981

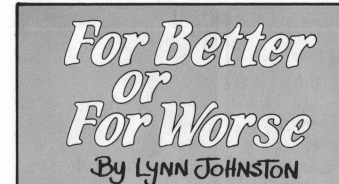

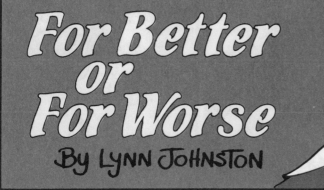

# For Better or For Worse

## By Lynn Johnston

GOOD NIGHT, MICHAEL.

MOM... WHO DO YOU LOVE MOST—ME OR ELIZABETH?

I LOVE YOU BOTH THE SAME, HONEY.

IF LOVE WAS A PIE— I BET DADDY WOULD GET THE BIGGEST PIECE.

MICHAEL, IF LOVE WAS A PIE, I'D CUT ALL THE PIECES THE SAME SIZE....

BUT TONIGHT—YOU'D GET THE FIRST PIECE.

LIFE'S GREAT—NO MATTER HOW YOU SLICE IT!

LYNN

November 22, 1981

# For Better or For Worse

## By Lynn Johnston

*Quality Clothes for Men*

DRESS PANTS

EXCUSE ME, BUT IF YOU'RE SHOPPING FOR HUBBY YOU WILL LOVE THESE PANTS! - HE TOSSES THEM ON THE FLOOR, - YOU TOSS THEM IN THE WASH AND VOILA` - READY TO WEAR! RIGHT OUT OF THE DRYER!

YOU NEVER NEED TO IRON THEM!

WHAT MAKES YOU THINK I DO THE IRONING? MY HUSBAND IS PERFECTLY CAPABLE OF IRONING HIS PANTS.

I CAN'T GET OVER THE FACT THAT PEOPLE AUTOMATICALLY ASSUME THAT THE WIFE DOES THESE THINGS!

IN THAT CASE - HOW ABOUT A COTTON OR WOOL BLEND?

UH....

I'LL TAKE THE PERMANENT PRESS.

November 29, 1981

# For Better or For Worse

## By Lynn Johnston

WELL, THEY COULDN'T STAY AT THE HOTEL, SEE ... SO THE MANAGER SAYS THEY CAN SLEEP IN THE BARN —

LOOK! BABY!

YEAH-A BABY.

SO, THEY GOT THE BABY, SEE, AN' THEY PUT HIM IN THE MANGER. AN' ANGELS WERE ON THE ROOF — AN' THERE WAS THIS STAR...

AN' THEN THESE THREE WISE GUYS 'CIDED TO BRING PRESENTS SO THEY GOT ON THEIR CAMELS AN' BROUGHT GOLD AN' TWO OTHER THINGS."

BY THIS TIME, THERE WAS SHEEP AN' FARMERS ALL OVER THE PLACE — WITH EVERYONE COMIN' IN TO SEE THE BABY!

MICHAEL, I DON'T THINK YOU'RE READING THAT STORY EXACTLY THE WAY IT'S WRITTEN!

I DON'T HAVE TO.

I KNOW IT OFF MY HEART!

February 21, 1982